The Bop

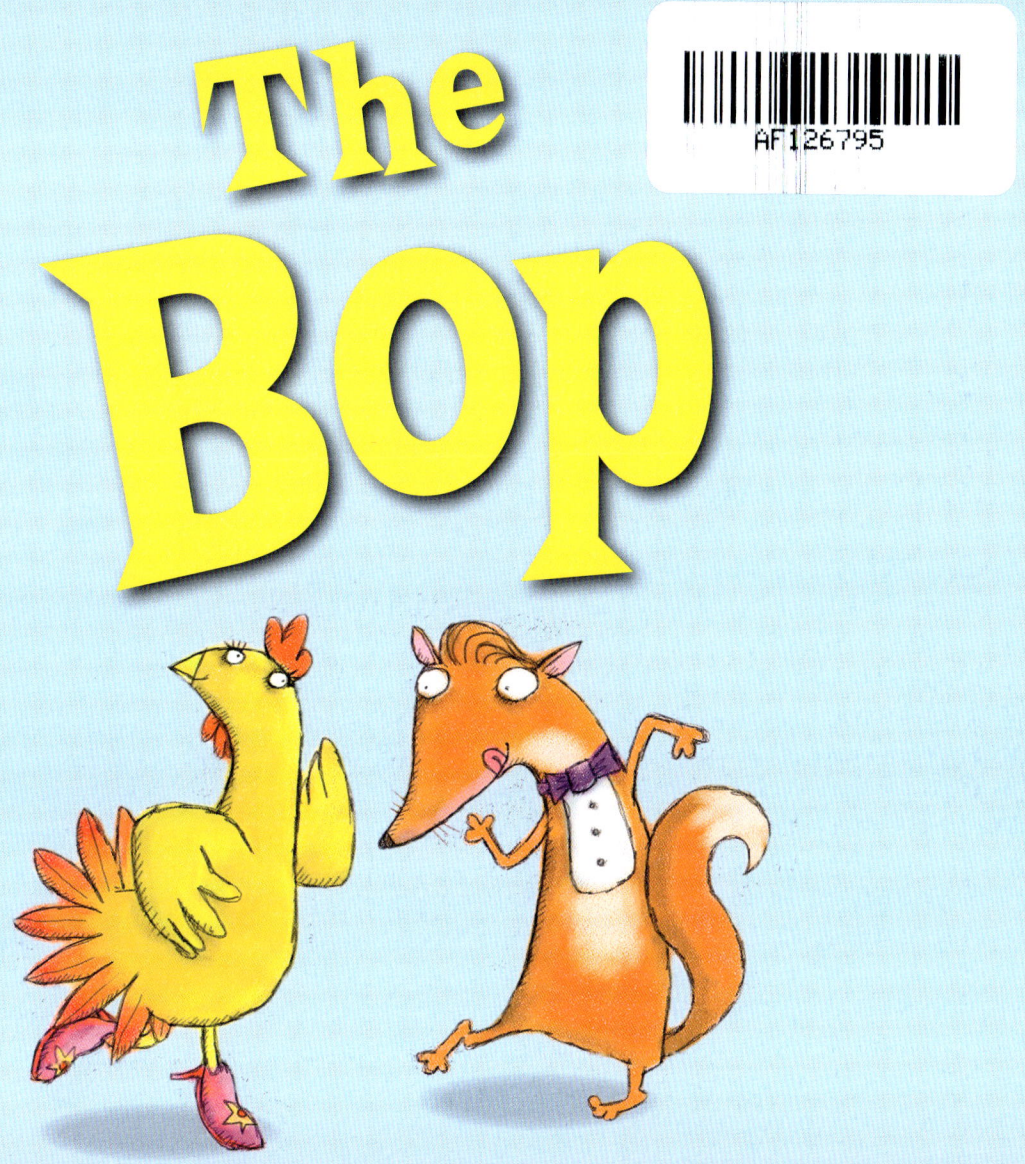

Written by Jeanne Willis
Illustrated by Lee Wildish

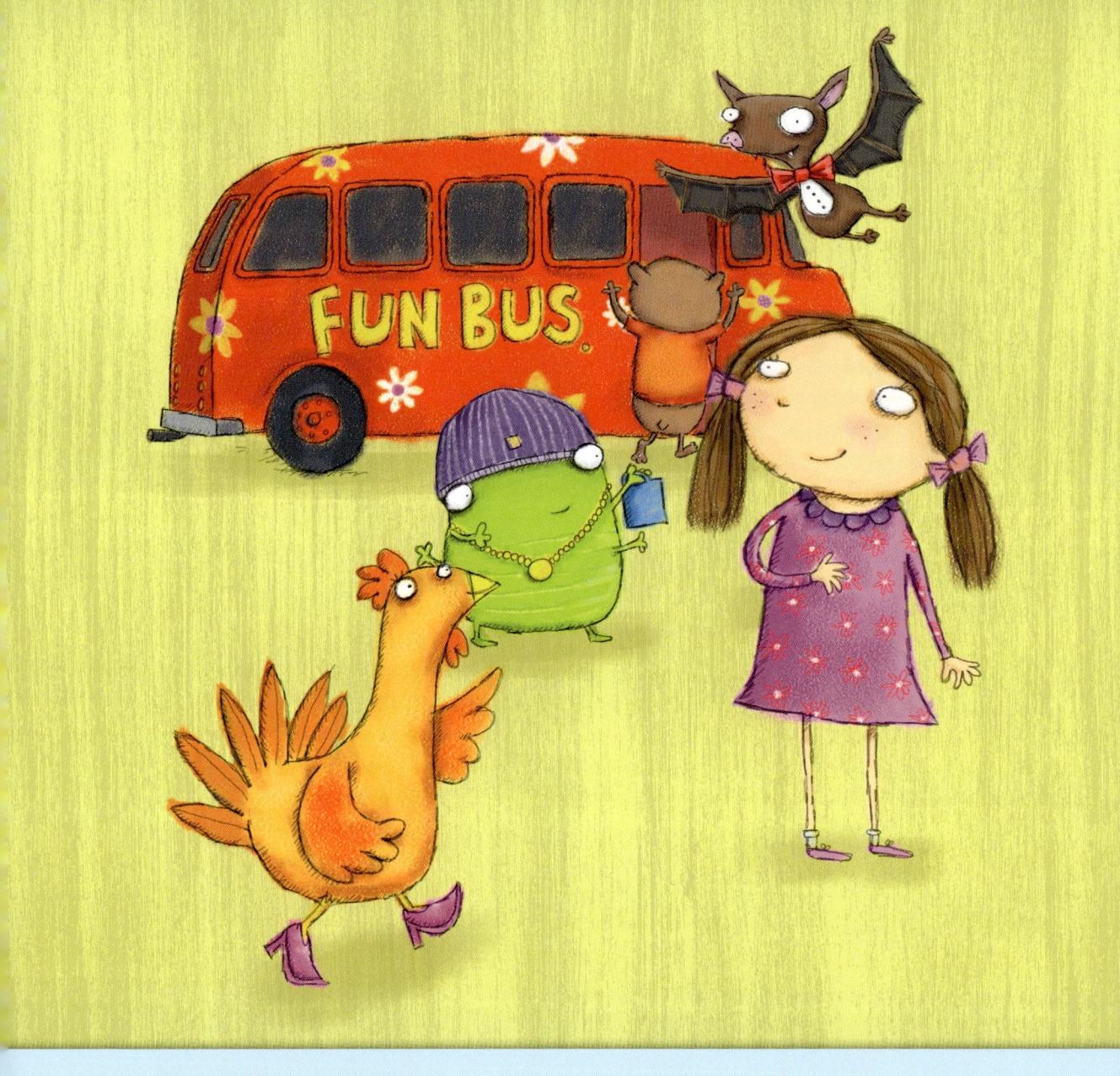

Let's get into the fun bus.

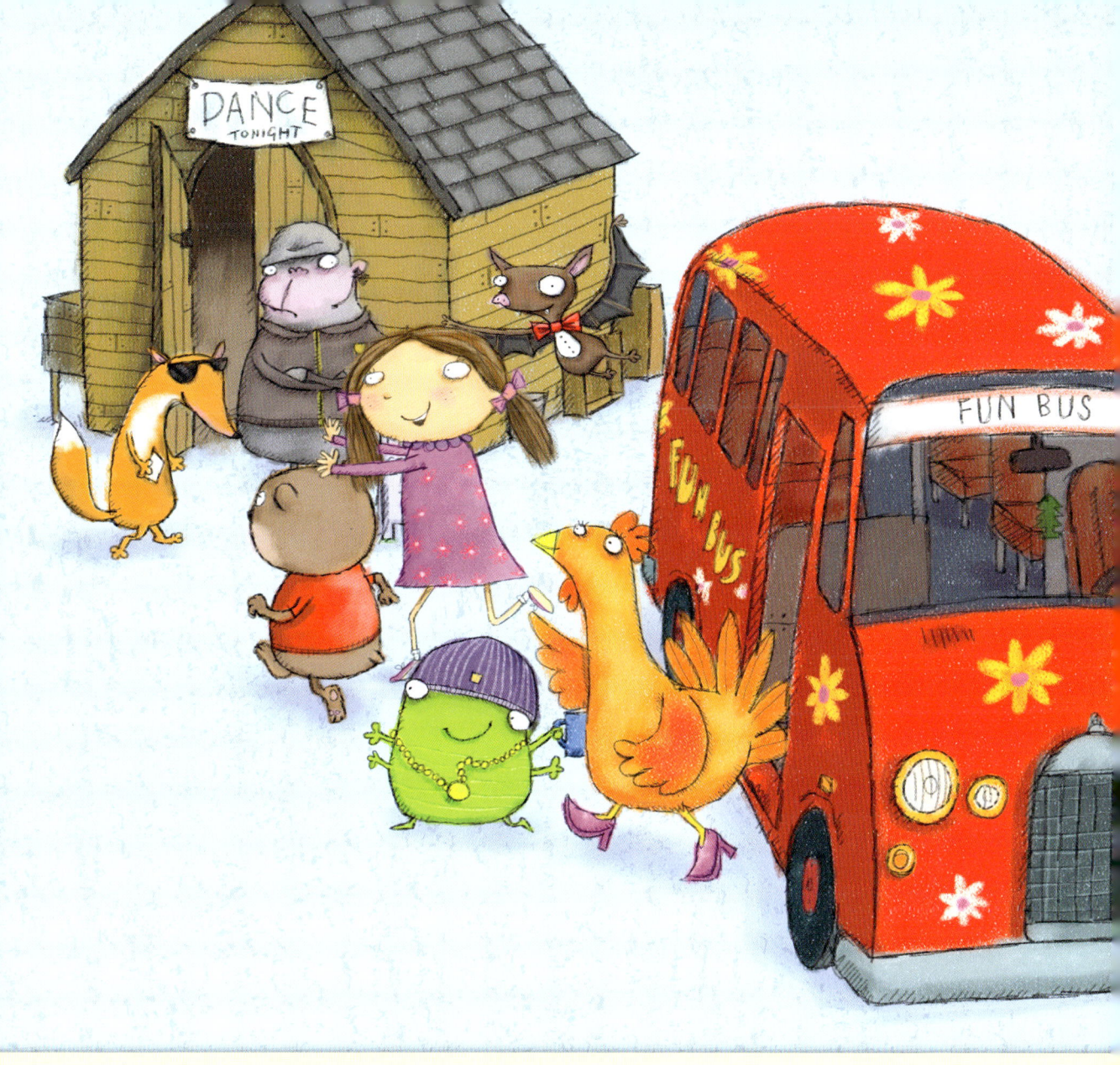

Go to the bop!

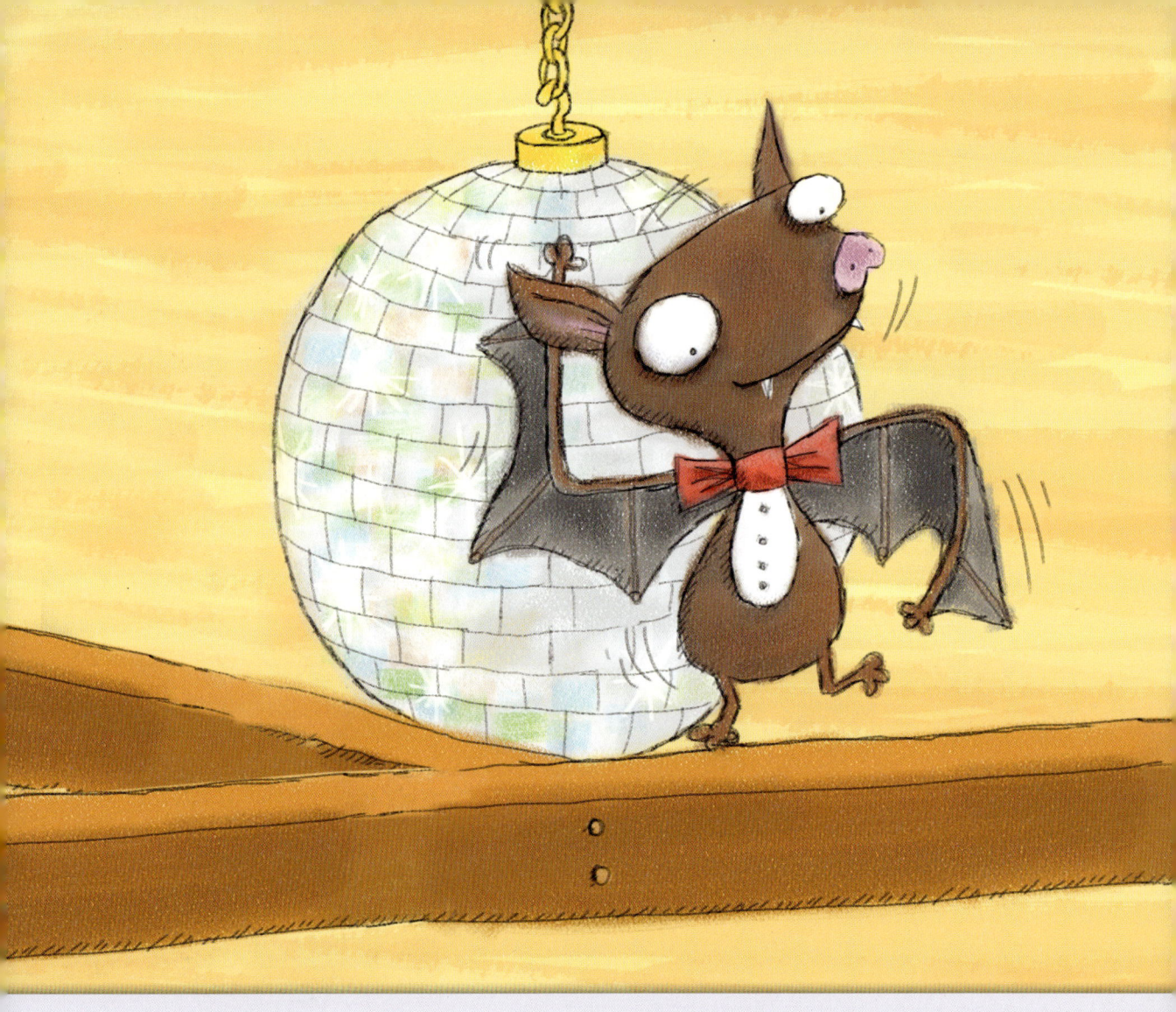

The bat can bob.
Bob, bob, bob!

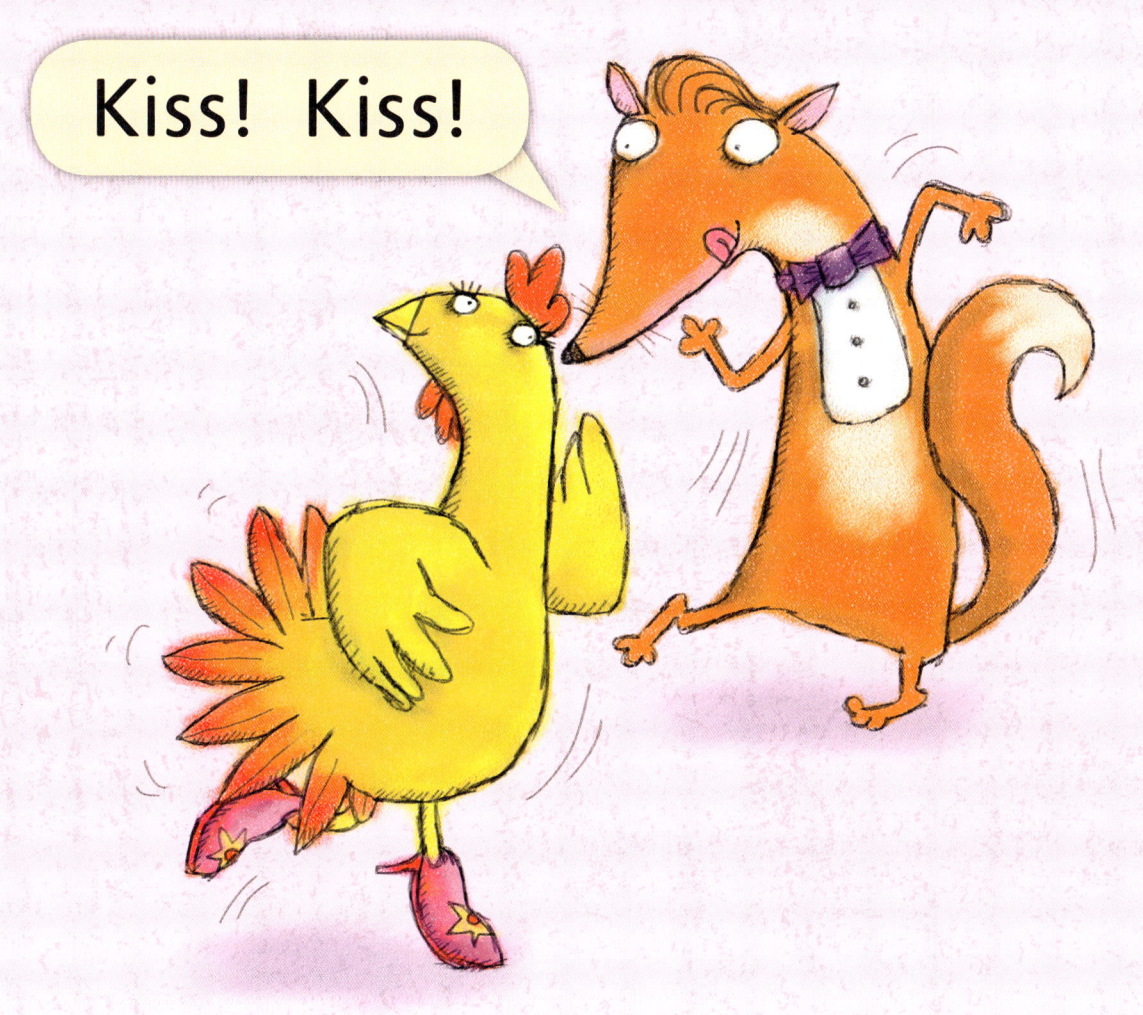

The hen can hop.
Hop, Hen, hop!

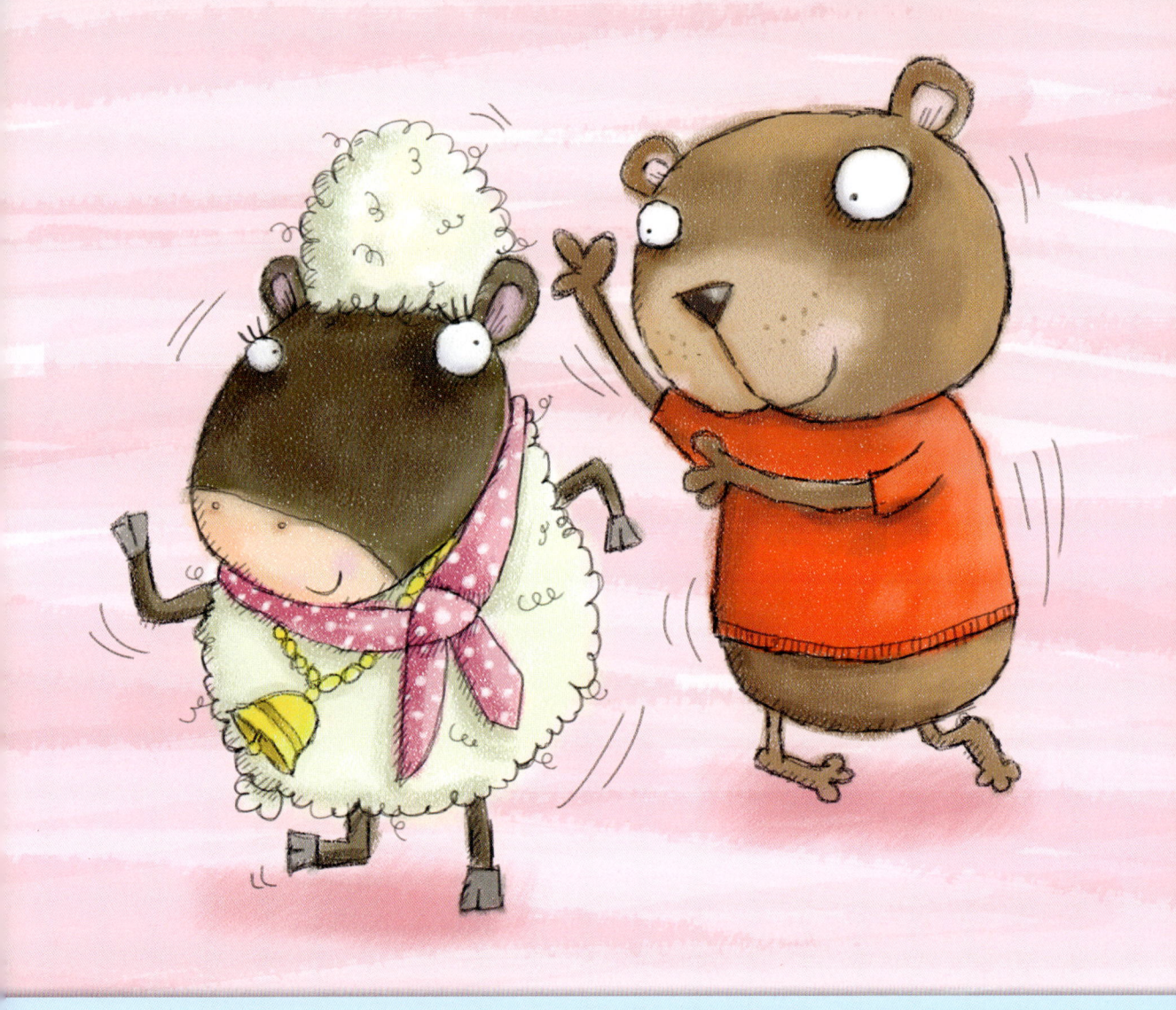

The cub can rock.
Rock it, Cub!

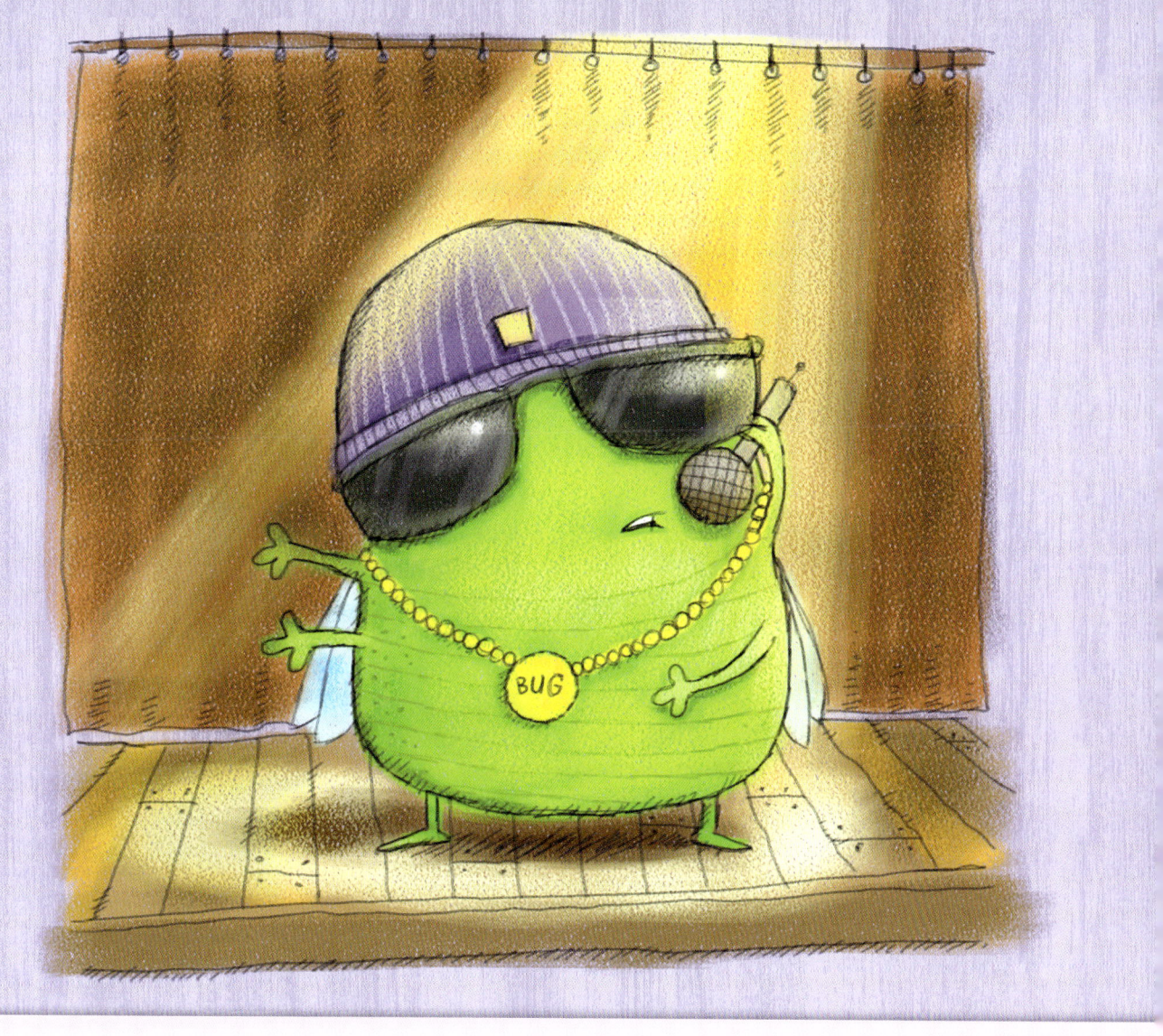

The bug can rap.
Rap, Bug, rap!

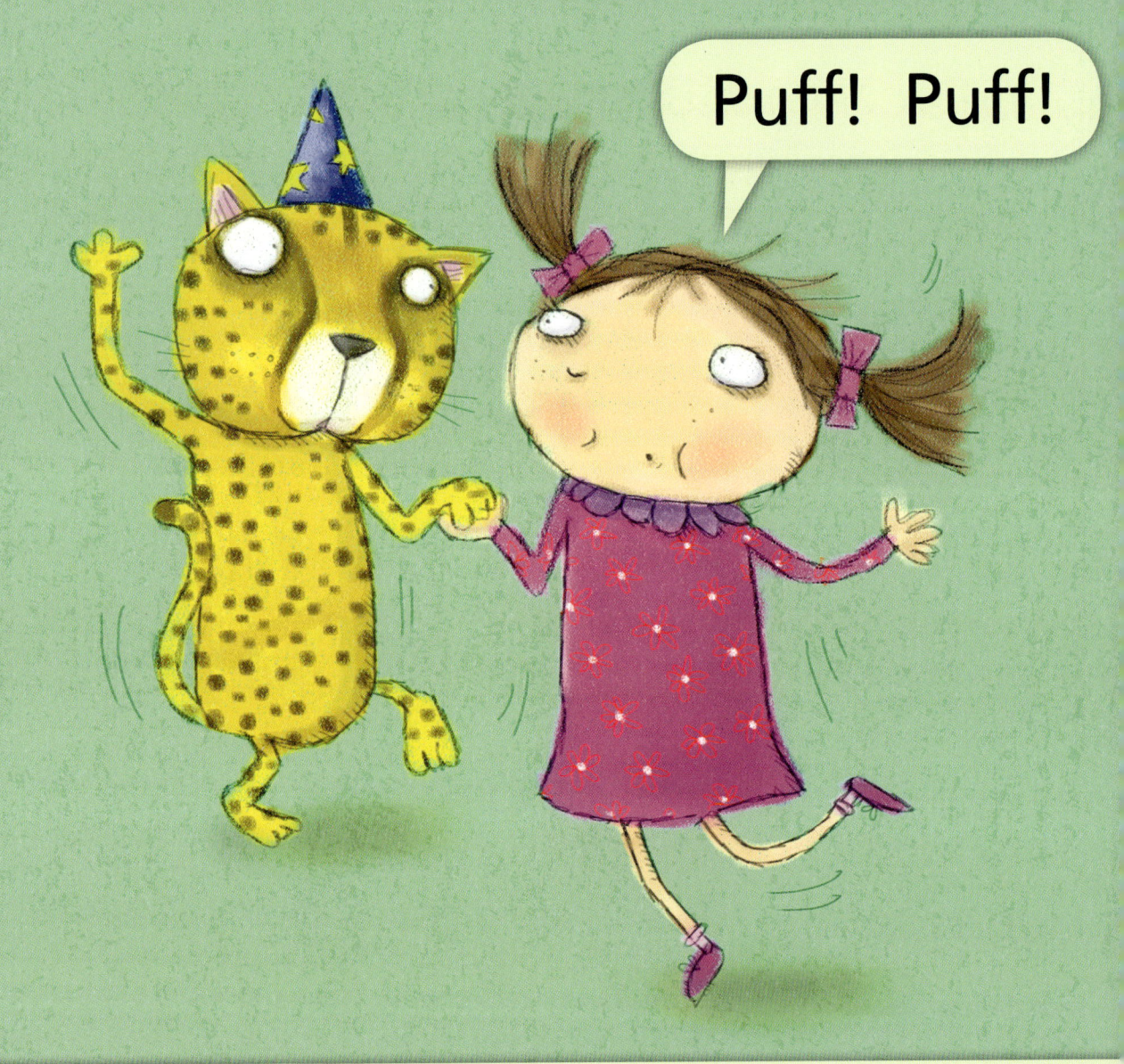

I can salsa!